This book belongs to

....

THE RUNT PIG

a collection of short stories

Copyright © 2010 by All About Learning Press
Printed in the United States of America

All About Learning Press
2038 E. Anvil Lake Road
Eagle River, WI 54521

ISBN 978-1-935197-11-9

Cover Design and Page Layout: David LaTulippe

Illustrations:

Matt Chapman:	"The Big Top" · "The Hit" · "The Runt Pig"
Donna Goeddaeus:	"Lost in the Bog" · "Slim Went West" · "Mud Milk"
	"The Ant Hill" · "The Big Mess" · "The Plan"
David LaTulippe:	"The Wind on the Hill" · "Fish Class"

Story idea for "Lost in the Bog": Donna Goeddaeus

The Runt Pig: a collection of short stories is part of the *All About Reading* program. For more books in this series, go to www.AllAboutReading.com.

To the reader –
enjoy your trip through this book!

Contents

Lost in the Bog

Gump was lost in the bog
at dusk.

Gump felt the mist.

Gump felt the wind.

But Gump went on.

Gump felt a bump.

It went past.

It was fast. Gasp!

Gump hid.

Is it an elf?

Is it a pest?

Is it a dog?

Is it...the end?

Gump must act fast.

Gump can run! That is it!

A dash! A rush! A jog!

But help — a hump!

A big hump

is in the path!

"GUMP!"

The bump is Sis!

The End

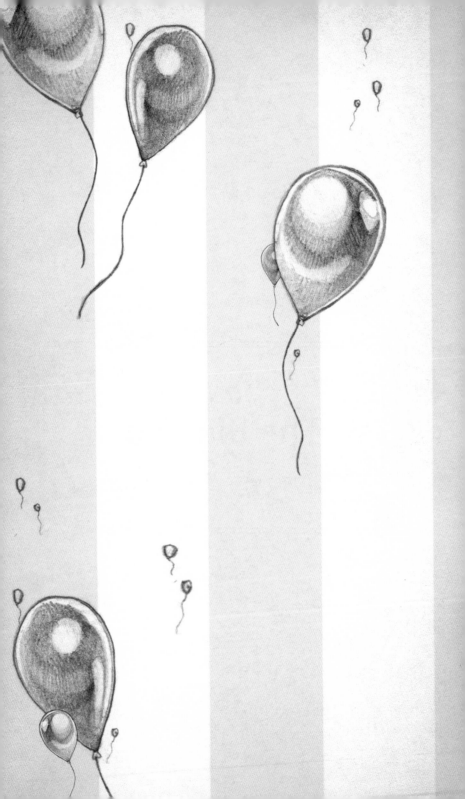

The Big Top

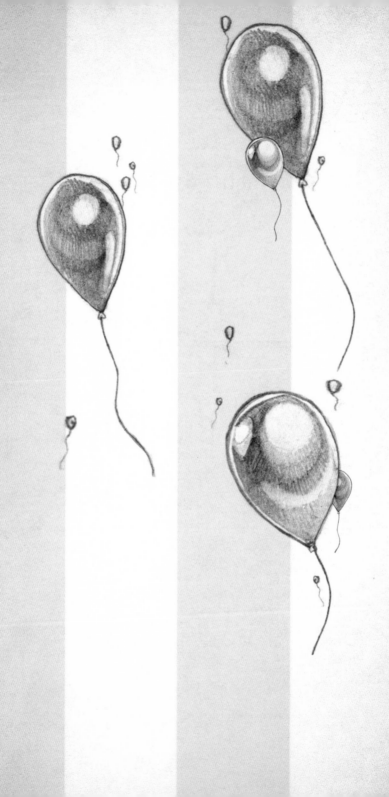

The tent is up.
The band is set.

"Bam, bam, bam!"

went the drum.

Dex and Silk trot fast.

Glen gets on the hump.

Stan and Pam run

and get a grip.

"Spot, jump on this pad."

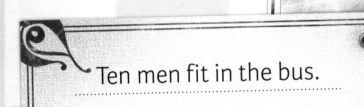

Ten men fit in the bus.

"The Blob" is a big man
and can lift a van.

Beth can run and flip fast.

Beth can land

next to the band.

A trip to the Big Top
is fun!

The End

Slim Went West

Slim had a map of the West.

It was a vast land.

Slim was not rich.

The man had just a map

and a hat.

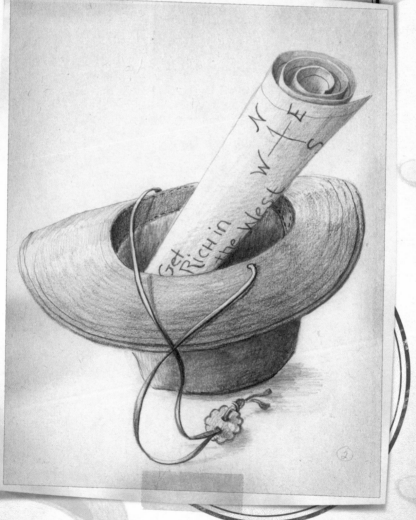

"I will get rich in the West."

Slim set off on a trip

with the map in his hand.

Is that a red rag?

This rag can help on the trip

to the West.

The rag can stop the dust.

The red rag is a lunch bag
at the end of a twig.

It is hot.

The rag can stop the sun.

A dog is lost. His leg has a cut.
Slim can help the dog
with the rag.

The dog can help Slim.

The dog will get an ax.

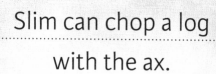

Slim can chop a log
with the ax.

The sun has set.

"I must stop at this tent,"
said Slim.

The dog and Slim
get in the tent.

Slim had his rag, a hat, a map, a tent, an ax, and a dog.

Slim *was* rich.

The End

Mud Milk

Add a bit of grass

and a dab of sand.

Mix it in a glass.

This milk is grand!

Cut up a red bud.

Mix in a pat of mud.

A shred of mint can add zest.

Bits of twigs — that is best.

Add this stem and that grit.

This fluff will fit!

Fill it to the top.

Then add this sand. Drop!

Mud milk will hit the spot!

The End

The Wind
on the Hill

"A big wind is on the hill!"
said Greg.

Bess and Greg ran up the hill.
Jazz went with them.
The kids and the frog sat
in the grass.

"I spot a hen in a nest!"
said Greg.

"Is that a fish on a dish?"
said Bess.

Next a man in his bath
sped past.

"It is an ox!"

said Bess with a grin.

"And a doll in a dress
is next to him," said Greg.

"A lot of fun stuff
is in the wind."

"I wish *I* was in the wind!"

said Bess.

"I will jump and spin!"

"I *am* in the wind!"

"Jazz, help us with the next gust of wind," said Bess.

"A wet ship! Run!" said Greg.

Then Bess and Greg and Jazz
ran off in a gust of wind.

The End

The Ant Hill

The ant had a plan.

The ant dug a path in the sand.

The ant dug and dug

in the sand.

The ant must not rest.

It is a big task,

but the ant has help.

Up the hill the ants went.

The ants left the sand

at the top of the hill.

The ants did not get lost.

Drag and drop.

Drag and drop the sand.

Bump and dump.

Bump and dump

a clump of sand.

Get a grip.

Get a grip on that grit!

The ant hill got big.

It got big fast!

It was a big task,
but the ants did it!

The End

The Hit

Tom is up at bat.

Can Tom hit it?

He hit it!

It was a big hit.

It went up and up.
It did not land!

At last it did land.

Can Tom and his pals find it?

Did it thud on the shed?

No.

Is it in the mulch?

No.

Did it drop in the grass?

No.

Did it land in the dog dish?

No.

Tom and his pals
did not find it.

It is in the nest!

The End

Fish Class

The fish went to class.

Class #1

The fish had math class.

Class #2

"If a net dips in the pond, swim to the hut — fast!" said Miss Flip.

Class #3

The fish swam laps
to get fit and trim.

Class #4

The fish jump up
and flip for fun.

Class #5

Miss Flip said, "This is a big bad cat. If the cat gets next to us, zig and zag. This cat will get us if it can!"

Class #6

This is the best class.
The fish tap the bell
to get fed!

At the end of class,

the fish nap.

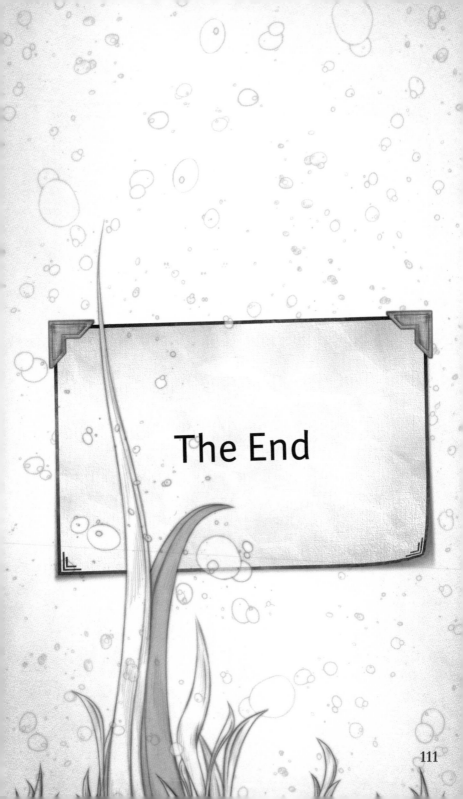

The End

The Big Mess

Sam has a mix.

Sam will mix it up in a pan.

Sam will add milk.

Sam will add an egg.

The egg will drop.

It will drip and glop.

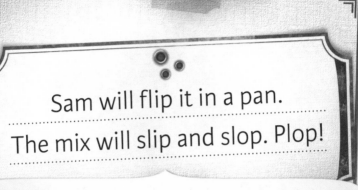

Sam will flip it in a pan.

The mix will slip and slop. Plop!

If the stuff gets stiff,

Mom will get mad.

Get a wet rag.

Get a damp mop.

Blot it. Mop it.

Get that big wet mess!

It is still a mess!

Get that drip.

Get that drop.

Sam did not stop.

Sam did not miss a spot.

Sam did the job well,
and Mom is glad.

The End

The Plan

Ann got a bed.

Gram has a plan.

Gram cut up a dress and a vest and a pant leg.

Gram cut up a cloth bag
and a bit of silk.

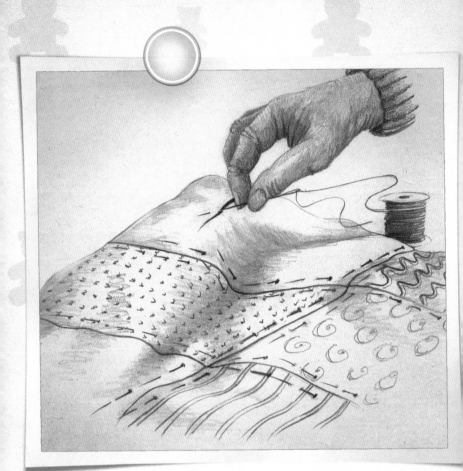

Gram did mend a rip.

Gram did pin and snip.

Gram must press it.

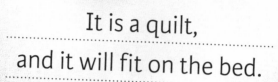

It is a quilt,
and it will fit on the bed.

Ann is glad!

The End

The Runt Pig

Bret is a runt pig.

Bret is slim, not fat.

Bret is not a big pig.

Bret is just a runt.

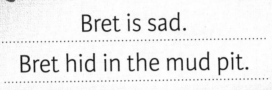

Bret is sad.

Bret hid in the mud pit.

"A rat is in the hen hut!

The rat will get the eggs!"

said Beth the Hen.

"Nell, help us! Get the rat!"
said Beth the Hen.

"But I will not fit

in the hen hut!" said Nell.

"Ted, help! Lend us a hand!

Get the rat!"

said Beth the Hen.

"But I will not fit

in the hen hut!" said Ted.

"Bev, lend us a hand! Help us!

The rat will get the eggs!"

said Beth the Hen.

"I will not fit up the ramp
to the hut!" said Bev.

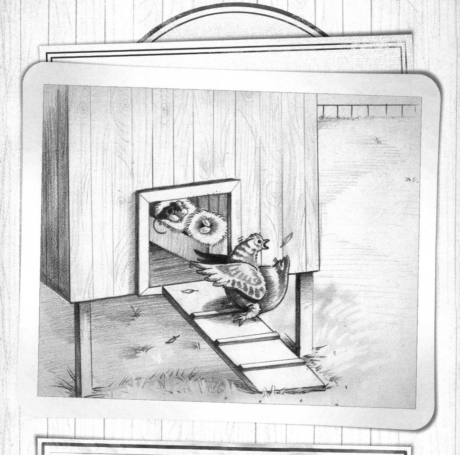

Beth the Hen said to Bev,
"Get Bret the Runt Pig!
Bret will fit! Bret can run
up the ramp and get the rat!"

Bev ran to get Bret the Runt Pig.

"Bret, help the hens!

A rat is in the hen hut. The rat

will get the eggs!" said Bev.

● ● ● ●

"I will stop him," said Bret.

The runt pig sped up the path.
Bret ran to the hen hut
and then up the ramp.

The rat sat in the nest
next to the eggs.

Bret hit the rat. Bop!
The rat ran.

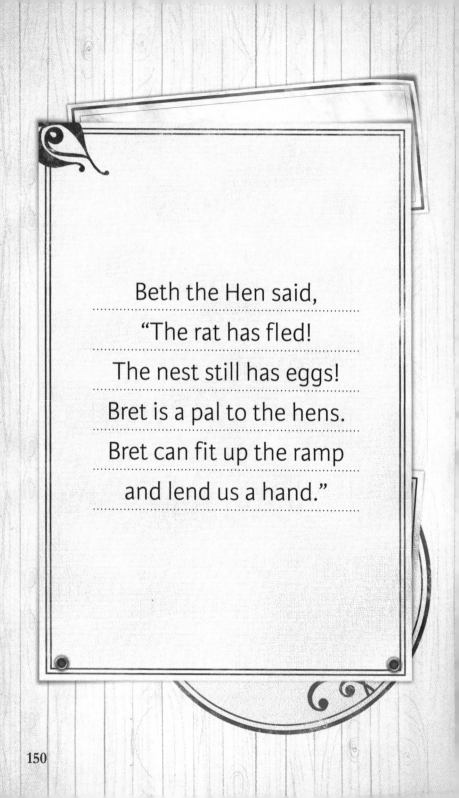

Beth the Hen said,

"The rat has fled!

The nest still has eggs!

Bret is a pal to the hens.

Bret can fit up the ramp

and lend us a hand."

The runt pig is not sad.

Bret is not big,

but Bret can still help.

The End

You did it!

You read the whole book!

What do you think of that?

Now it's time to read

Cobweb the Cat!